Cont... C0-ASB-571

Chapter 1

The Storm

The storm tossed our ship at sea. Waves battered its wooden sides. Two of my brothers, Ernest and Jack, held on to each other in a corner. Mother and Father held my other brother, Franz. The three of them sat between two tubs.

I, Fritz, was the oldest of the four boys. I had to be brave.

*How quickly the storm had steered us away from the land we were headed to! We were hoping to bring the goodness of Switzerland, our home, to a new country. On board our ship were many kinds of plants and trees.

Bushes and flowers were stacked in corners of the boat. We had animals with us too. Ducks, cows, goats,* and hens could be heard day and night. Grains and meats were packed in boxes. We had all we needed. Little did we know how quickly things could change.

Suddenly the captain yelled, "We are lost!" Sailors began to jump off the ship. We went up the ladder to the main deck. There we found the last sailor jumping into the last lifeboat.

Cowards! We were a family with children. And they had left us behind.

The storm went on for hours. At last the ship came to a stop. Soon the rain slowed and the thunder ended. Father sent us below deck. We were all so tired that no one could even speak.

Mother held little Franz in her arms. My other brothers and I fell asleep on some mats.

Chapter 2

Island Ho!

*I woke to animal sounds. My dog, Turk, licked my hand. I walked up on deck.

In the warm sunlight, I saw that our ship was stuck between two big rocks. And land was not far away! The rocks had saved our lives. Had we jumped into the sea with the sailors, we would have died.

After looking things over,* Father came up with a plan. We found four wooden tubs. We dropped them into the water. These tubs would float us safely to shore.

We would have to leave the animals for now. Turk barked from the ship as we left. Then he jumped in the water and paddled along next to us.

We cheered when we reached the sandy beach. At last we were out of harm's way. I could see tall coconut trees through a spyglass I had grabbed from the captain's desk.

Father told me to follow him around the rocky bank. He said we should look to see if any sailors had made it to shore.

I was upset. "Why should we care at all about them, Father?" I said. "They left us!"

"Two wrongs can never make a right, Fritz," he said. "Also, we need all the help we can get. If we find anyone, we need to do the right thing—for their sake and for our own."

—Chapter 3—

Falconhurst

*Mother felt a tree house was the best plan for a safe home. We needed shade from the sun. So we headed into the thick woods. We crossed a wide stream. Then we saw the biggest tree I had ever seen. It would be our new home. It was about 200 feet from the beach.

We got right to work.* Father made a ladder out of bamboo. He sent the rest of us out to find sticks, leaves, and branches. He told us the house could not be built without them.

Within three weeks, our new home had rooms with floors and windows. It was the best!

Mother planned for steps to be built inside the trunk of the tree. Our front door came from the ship.

Once, while we were working on the trunk, bees came after us. We had taken their home. We ran for shelter. But we were stung many times. Jack got stung on his left cheek.

Father made a new hive for the bees about 150 feet away. After two days they buzzed to their new home. We ate the honey they left behind.

We built the very top of our home last. It was a small deck. Father cleared away overhead branches and leaves. From there we could see the stars at night.

We were like birds in a nest. We called our home "Falconhurst."

Chapter 4

Monkey See, Monkey Do

One morning Father and I came upon some monkeys in the coconut trees. Father said that coconuts had sweet, warm milk inside them.

*"But how do we get the coconuts out of the trees?" I asked. Father looked at me and smiled.

He tossed some rocks up in the trees. Right away, the monkeys started to move around in the trees. Then coconuts came falling down!

Father and I laughed. We put our hands on our heads until the monkeys stopped shaking the* trees.

We cracked open a coconut. The milk inside was good. We took home all we could carry.

One day, near the coconut trees, I found a baby monkey. I named him Max. We also found two pet frogs. We named them Rocky and Rolly.

Ernest trained a green parrot that he named Bob. He had found it near a nest in a tree. Jack found a small horse. We called her Bella. We also had two rabbits named Rex and Buster.

Rusty, our pet fox, was the animal Franz liked best. Our animal friends were fun and sometimes helpful.

Chapter 5

Let the Games Begin

Jack and Ernest began thinking that all the animals should race one another. We started with a relay. We had teams working in twos or threes. Father said he would keep time. Turk had Max on his back. Little Franz was on my back, and I was riding a donkey. Jack was riding a cow. Ernest was riding an ostrich.

Father lined us up. "On your marks, get set, GO!" he said. Turk and Max started running across the beach.

*Ernest's ostrich took a few big leaps. Then it went around and around in the sand, making Ernest sick. The cow never moved. So Jack left her and grabbed a pig. At first he seemed to be riding the pig. But then we saw that he was carrying it! My donkey didn't move at all.

Turk and Max won the* relay with no help from any of us.

We ran more races the rest of the day. We also had a contest to see who could find the most clams. Mother handed the winners shiny medals she had found on the ship.

At the end of the day we put the animals in the little homes we had built for them. Then Father cooked some wild goose over a fire on the beach. Mother made flat bread and sweet apples.

We ate and laughed until we could hardly move. This was one of the best days on our island.

Chapter 6

My Grand Find

Ten years passed by quickly on the island. I was 23 years old and I longed to go to other parts of the island alone. Father understood. I had become a man. After saying good-bye to my family, I headed for parts of the island we had never been to.

After two months Father came looking for me. I was happy to see him. I told him stories of hunting and exploring caves. But I saved my best story for last.

While fishing one day, I had found another person! He was looking for clams. His name was Edward. He had been on his own for a long time. His father was a British army man. Their ship had gone down three years ago. Edward was the only one who had made it to shore.

Edward had been on the island alone for three years. He fished. He sang himself to sleep. But he was very lonely. Then I met him and became his friend.

*After Father met Edward, he said we should all go back to Falconhurst right away. Mother would be glad to see me.

When we returned, Franz ran to me. He was now 17 years old. He jumped on me and we fell to the sand, laughing. After Edward met Jack and Ernest, we ate and talked long into the night.*

The next morning Mother spoke with Edward. Edward told Mother about a young girl who had washed up on the shore that night three years ago.

In order to be safe on the island, the girl pretended to be a young man. For three years she dressed in men's clothes. She spoke and acted like a young man.

Then Edward told Mother that he was that young girl! Her name was really Jenny Montrose.

Jenny had played the part very well. Until that day, I did not know that Edward, my brave friend, was really a girl. My brothers didn't know what to say.

It was clear to Mother and Father that for me, things were not the same after Jenny told me who she really was. I knew that I loved her.

It was not long after this that I told Jenny how I felt. She told me that she loved me too.

We stood on the beach and watched the tide come in. We made plans for our life on the island. Then we saw something at sea. It was a ship!

We ran to Father and Mother. Our whole family, even the animals, rushed to the shore.

When the ship came close, Father went to greet it with one of our rafts. The sailors cheered when they saw him.

After so many years on the island, we were saved. But the island had become a part of us. It was our home.

Afterword

The Robinson family was rescued. But not everyone left the island.

Fritz and Jenny went back to her father's family in England. Franz planned to go to school. Jack and Ernest stayed on the island. Mother and Father Robinson also stayed on the island for the rest of their lives.

Jenny and Fritz made a map to the island. They returned to it many times. They also took other people with them to the island. The people wanted to see how they could have lived on it for so long.

And every time Fritz went back to the island, part of him wanted to stay.